This book belongs to

....

....

ISBN 978-0-6456040-7-8

Join Jackson's Journey further at
www.joinjacksonsjourney.com.au

There are many different views on best practice leadership.
The strategies shared in this book have been written from my
experience as a leader, a leadership coach, and as a mother
of a little boy who we want to see develop into a leader in his
preferred field, and for him to reach for the stars.

Published in Australia by Ingram Spark
https://www.ingramspark.com

Asking for Help

By Renata Roberts
Illustrated by Josefina Luna

TIPS FOR THE READER

Four steps to get the most out of joining Jackson's journey...

STEP 1

Before reading Jackson's journey, go to the last page and read the key learnings from this book. Take time to understand them yourself.

STEP 2

Now find a comfortable place to take your little learner through the story, reading aloud and talking about what is happening in the pictures.

STEP

3

As you come to the part of the story where a key learning is experienced by Jackson, help your learner to understand this more by reinforcing the importance of the lesson.

STEP

4

At the end, take time to talk through the key learnings again, referring this time to how your little learner might do this themselves.

It is a beautiful sunny day and Jackson is going to the beach with Mummy and Daddy.

Jackson loves to play at the beach.

Jackson has lots of beach toys that he can play with on the sand. He has spades, buckets, and moulds of all different shapes to build sandcastles.

Jackson loves to
make sandcastles.

Sometimes he will
build a big sandcastle
with all the different
moulds he owns.
Jackson likes to put
shells over the castle
to decorate it and dig
a big trench so he can
fill it with water.

"Look what I have set up," Daddy calls out
to Jackson.

Daddy had set up the volleyball
net and was throwing the ball
in the air pretending to serve
it toward Jackson.

"Want to have a game, Jackson?"
Daddy asked him.

Jackson, Daddy
and Mummy
played volleyball
for a long time.

Soon it was time to leave the beach and go home.

Jackson started to pack up his toys stacking into his arms the buckets, his sand moulds, and his spades.

There were so many toys to carry.

As Jackson bent down to pick up the final spade, he dropped all the toys back on the sand except one bucket and two spades.

Jackson had to start all over again.

"Jackson, can I help you?" Mummy asked.

"No, thank you. I can do this myself," Jackson insisted. He was determined that he didn't need anyone to help him carry his toys.

Jackson was wrong though.

He couldn't do it himself.

The same thing happened just as he was
about to pick up the last spade —
everything fell to the ground.

Jackson was upset and sat on the sand
disappointed.

"Jackson, did you think this might be a good time to ask Mummy for help? Maybe I could help you carry some of the toys."

"But I want to do it myself. I know I can do it myself!"

"I understand that Jackson, but there are too many for you to pick up all at once on your own. You could either do multiple trips, or you could ask Mummy for help to load the toys into your arms. It would make me feel happy to be able to help you."

Jackson thought this was a good idea.

"Can you please help to pick up my toys and put them in my arms so I can carry all of them myself?"

With his Mummy's help, Jackson was able to carry ALL of the toys on his own back to the beach trolley.

Jackson just needed to
ask for help to be able to
achieve what he wanted to do.

Jackson was pleased that
Mummy felt good being asked
to help.

These are the KEY LEARNINGS you will find in this journey of Jackson's...

It is ok to ask for help. It is not a sign of weakness.

We will all be in a place where we need help one day, and learning how to ask for help before everything starts to drop around us is better than waiting for it to fall.

Make your question for help sound more like a positive. After all, when you ask someone to help you, you are giving them the opportunity to do something nice and sometimes for them to learn new things.

If people see you ask for help, it is more likely they will feel comfortable asking for help from you one day when they need it.

There are many journeys to take with Jackson as he learns...

LEARNING FROM MISTAKES

Jackson learns how mistakes do happen, but it is what you do from there that is important for every great leader to adopt.

SHOWING EMPATHY

Read how Jackson learns what empathy is and how to, as great leaders do, show empathy to others.

PREVENTING UNCONSCIOUS BIAS

Jackson finds out what unconscious bias is and how, as great leaders do, we can prevent it from occurring.

BEING INCLUSIVE

Join Jackson in learning why it is important to include people even if they are different from us and how, as great leaders do, we can be inclusive.

SOLVING PROBLEMS

Jackson will learn what techniques can help someone be better at solving problems.

MANAGING RISKS

Jackson learns how the underlying concepts of managing risk are not difficult and how important it is to do this every day.

ACTIVELY LISTENING

In this book, you will read how Jackson learns what actively listening is and how, as great leaders do, we make sure we demonstrate this skill.

BEING SELFLESS

Jackson will learn how important it is to not let your own ego get in the way of focusing on the mission and those who will accomplish it most successfully.

ASKING FOR HELP

Jackson learns how asking for help may be daunting, but with this act of vulnerability, a great leader can demonstrate mutual benefit where someone else has an opportunity to showcase their skills.

COURAGEOUS CONVERSATIONS

Jackson will learn how we will face having to have a conversation that will take courage, and that we need to not avoid these discussions.

MANAGING CHANGE

Read how Jackson learns how leaders can manage change effectively and how important it is that they positively influence any change that occurs.

BEING CREATIVE

Join Jackson as he learns how creative leaders can look at things in new ways and solve problems by seeing things others don't.

CELEBRATING SUCCESS

Join this journey as Jackson finds out that by celebrating our success, we reinforce the motivation that will carry us through to the next achievement, and how every great leader understands this is important to take the time to do.

RECEIVING FEEDBACK WELL

Jackson will learn how getting feedback can help us to grow, and therefore it is important to accept feedback by listening to what is said and reflecting on any improvements you can make.

BEING A POSITIVE INFLUENCE

Jackson learns on a rainy day how leaders demonstrate positive influence through both their behaviour and overall attitude, and when leaders do have a positive influence they create an environment where people are emotionally invested.

LEARNING THROUGH SELF REFLECTION

Jackson will learn how self-reflection in leadership means devoting time to think about yourself as a leader and is critical for leadership development.

EFFECTIVELY COMMUNICATING

Join Jackson as he learns how communication is one of the most important skills a leader can have and how it takes purpose and intention to implement effective communication.

EFFECTIVE NEGOTIATING

Jackson will learn how in negotiation, effective leaders seek to understand the interests of those they lead and find ways of satisfying those interests in order to achieve the desired goals.

MANAGING CONFLICT

Jackson learns how leaders can deal with conflict every day, and that this is ok, so long as the leader addresses the conflict and handles conflict efficiently and fairly.

ASKING QUESTIONS

Jackson will learn how asking questions is essential for building empathy, understanding, and trust — all of which are necessary for team success.

Printed in the USA
CPSIA information can be obtained
at www.ICGtesting.com
LVHW071520130624
783150LV00001B/6